# CLASSICS
## Illustrated ®

## Jules Verne
# FROM THE EARTH TO THE MOON

essay by
Gregory Feeley

## ACCLAIM BOOKS
### STUDY GUIDE

# .CLASSICS.
### Illustrated®

From The Earth To The Moon

art by Alex Blum
cover by Jim Calafiore

*For Classics Illustrated Study Guides*
computer recoloring by VanHook Studios
editor: Madeleine Robins
assistant editor: Gregg Sanderson
design: Scott Friedlander

Dale-Chall R.L.: 7.8

ISBN 1-57840-035-X

Acclaim Books, New York, NY
Printed in the United States

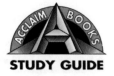

**STUDY GUIDE**

# FROM THE EARTH TO THE MOON
## By Jules Verne

HIGH ABOVE THE EARTH BECKONS THE MOST MYSTERIOUS LAND IN THE UNIVERSE... THE MOON. SINCE MAN'S FIRST NIGHT ON EARTH, HE HAS WONDERED ABOUT THIS GREAT LAMP THAT HANGS IN THE SKY. THE MOON WAS FEARED BY SOME, WORSHIPED BY OTHERS. WHAT IS THE HISTORY OF THE MOON? WHO LIVES ON ITS CELESTIAL SHORES? HERE IS THE STORY OF A BAND OF BRAVE MEN WHO RISKED THEIR LIVES AND FORTUNES TO PROBE THE SECRETS OF ... *THE MOON!*

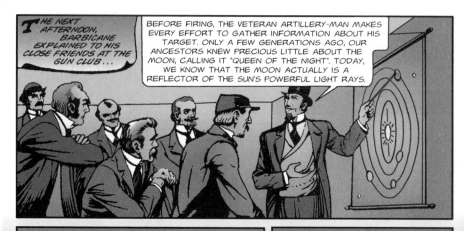

**T**HE NEXT AFTERNOON, BARBICANE EXPLAINED TO HIS CLOSE FRIENDS AT THE GUN CLUB...

BEFORE FIRING, THE VETERAN ARTILLERY-MAN MAKES EVERY EFFORT TO GATHER INFORMATION ABOUT HIS TARGET. ONLY A FEW GENERATIONS AGO, OUR ANCESTORS KNEW PRECIOUS LITTLE ABOUT THE MOON, CALLING IT "QUEEN OF THE NIGHT". TODAY, WE KNOW THAT THE MOON ACTUALLY IS A REFLECTOR OF THE SUN'S POWERFUL LIGHT RAYS.

"...EIGHT HEAVENLY BODIES REVOLVE IN A GREAT CIRCLE AROUND THE SUN. THEY ARE URANUS, SATURN, JUPITER, NEPTUNE, MERCURY, MARS, VENUS, AND OUR OWN EARTH. THEY REVOLVE IN THIS ETERNAL CIRCLE BECAUSE THE SUN EXERTS A PULLING FORCE KNOWN AS GRAVITY UPON THEM...

"...AS THEY REVOLVE AROUND THE SUN, SO DO SMALLER BODIES CIRCLE AROUND THEM. URANUS HAS EIGHT SATELLITES. SATURN EIGHT, JUPITER FOUR, NEPTUNE POSSIBLY THREE, AND THE EARTH ONE. THIS LAST WE CALL THE MOON...

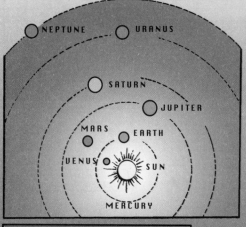

NEPTUNE
URANUS
SATURN
JUPITER
MARS
EARTH
VENUS
SUN
MERCURY

NEPTUNE-3 MOONS
SATURN-8 MOONS
JUPITER-4 MOONS
MOON
EARTH

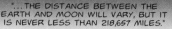

"...THE DISTANCE BETWEEN THE EARTH AND MOON WILL VARY, BUT IT IS NEVER LESS THAN 218,657 MILES."

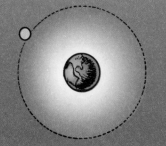

ACCORDING TO MY CALCULATIONS, WE CAN BOMBARD THE MOON WITH A GUN 900 FEET IN LENGTH, CAPABLE OF HOLDING 400,000 POUNDS OF HIGH EXPLOSIVES, AND DESIGNED TO FIRE AN ALUMINUM CANNON BALL WEIGHING 19,250 POUNDS.

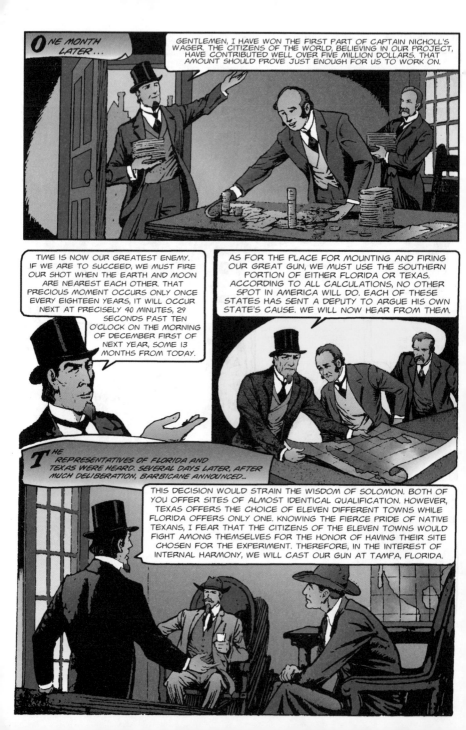

SEARCHING FOR JUST THE RIGHT SPOT TO CAST AND MOUNT THE GUN...

NOT EXACTLY A FIRM LOCATION TO POUR A CAST IRON GUN.

A POOR SPOT, THIS. YONDER PLATEAU MAY BE A MORE LIKELY PLACE. IT IS CALLED STONES HILL.

AT THE TOP OF STONES HILL...

THIS IS SURELY A FINE LOCATION.

THE SOIL APPEARS TO CONTAIN MUCH CLAY AND IS IDEAL FOR OUR PURPOSE. THIS LARGE PLAIN COULD ACCOMODATE OUR WORKSHOPS, FURNACES AND WORKMEN'S HUTS. YES, I HAVE DECIDED. FROM THIS PLACE SHALL OUR SHELL BEGIN ITS PERILOUS FLIGHT INTO THE OUTER REGIONS OF THE SOLAR WORLD.

BY THE END OF A MONTH, STONES HILL GUN STATION WAS READY FOR OPERATION. FIFTEEN HUNDRED SKILLED MEN CAME TO WORK FOR THE HIGH PAY AND CONSIDERABLE BONUSES OFFERED BY THE BALTIMORE GUN CLUB.

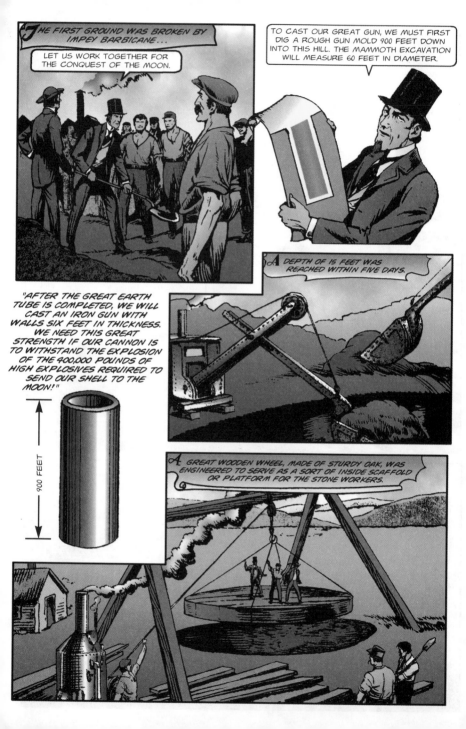

I WONDER IF MICHEL ARDAN IS FAMILIAR WITH THE TERRIBLE NATURE OF THE MOON?

"THE MOON IS RIDDLED WITH GREAT CRATERS, PROBABLY DUE TO VOLCANIC ERUPTIONS THAT TOOK PLACE SOME SEVERAL MILLION YEARS AGO."

"ALSO, WE HAVE THE GREAT MOUNTAINS OF THE MOON. ASTRONOMERS HAVE ESTIMATED THE PEAKS TO RISE SOME 22,606 FEET."

DO YOU BELIEVE THE MOON IS INHABITED?

NO ASTRONOMER HAS EVER SEEN SIGNS OF LIFE ON THE SURFACE OF THE MOON. PERHAPS MICHEL ARDAN WILL BE ABLE TO ANSWER THAT QUESTION SOMEDAY.

ON OCTOBER 20TH, MICHEL ARDAN'S SHIP ARRIVED AT TAMPA FROM FRANCE. A GREAT CROWD WAITED TO SEE WHAT THIS MAN, WHO WANTED TO BE SHOT TO THE MOON, LOOKED LIKE.

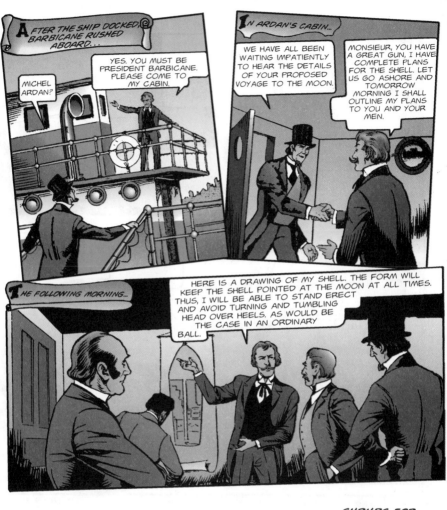

AFTER THE SHIP DOCKED, BARBICANE RUSHED ABOARD...

MICHEL ARDAN?

YES. YOU MUST BE PRESIDENT BARBICANE. PLEASE COME TO MY CABIN.

IN ARDAN'S CABIN...

WE HAVE ALL BEEN WAITING IMPATIENTLY TO HEAR THE DETAILS OF YOUR PROPOSED VOYAGE TO THE MOON.

MONSIEUR, YOU HAVE A GREAT GUN, I HAVE COMPLETE PLANS FOR THE SHELL. LET US GO ASHORE AND TOMORROW MORNING I SHALL OUTLINE MY PLANS TO YOU AND YOUR MEN.

THE FOLLOWING MORNING...

HERE IS A DRAWING OF MY SHELL. THE FORM WILL KEEP THE SHELL POINTED AT THE MOON AT ALL TIMES. THUS, I WILL BE ABLE TO STAND ERECT AND AVOID TURNING AND TUMBLING HEAD OVER HEELS. AS WOULD BE THE CASE IN AN ORDINARY BALL.

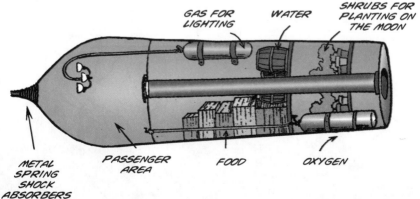

GAS FOR LIGHTING

WATER

SHRUBS FOR PLANTING ON THE MOON

METAL SPRING SHOCK ABSORBERS

PASSENGER AREA

FOOD

OXYGEN

THAT NIGHT, A MEETING WAS HELD IN ARDAN'S HOTEL ROOM...

WHAT A SET-BACK FOR SCIENCE IF EITHER BARBICANE OR NICHOLL IS KILLED IN THIS DUEL.

IT'S AN AFFAIR OF HONOR.

THEY'VE BEEN ENEMIES FOR YEARS. WHAT CAN WE DO?

LET ME REMIND YOU HOW HORRIBLE A FOREST DUEL WITH RIFLES CAN BE. EACH MAN BECOMES A MANHUNTER.

"IMAGINE THE TWO ENEMIES, EACH ARMED WITH A HIGH-POWERED RIFLE, TRACKING EACH OTHER DOWN LIKE WILD BEASTS!"

"A FATAL AMBUSH IS THE TRAP, AND DEATH IS THE REWARD!"

I MUST SAVE THE LIVES OF BARBICANE AND NICHOLL. SOMEHOW, I MUST CONVINCE THEM TO GIVE UP THIS DEADLY MANHUNT!

GOOD LUCK!

ONWARD, ARDAN REACHED THE FOREST. HE CLIMBED INTO A TALL TREE AND SCANNED THE FOREST WITH HIS BINOCULARS...

THERE'S CAPTAIN NICHOLL.

CAPTAIN NICHOLL WAS STRUGGLING TO FREE A LARGE AND BEAUTIFUL BIRD FROM THE DEADLY WEB OF A GIANT TROPICAL SPIDER...

ARDAN HURRIED TO NICHOLL'S SIDE.

YOU HAVE BEEN MERCIFUL TO THAT BIRD. WHY DON'T YOU SHOW THE SAME MERCY TO BARBICANE? CALL OFF THIS TERRIBLE DUEL, AND I WILL MAKE YOU A MOST FASCINATING PROPOSITION!

WHAT IS YOUR PROPOSITION?

I HAVE SUCH A TREMENDOUS OFFER THAT IT CAN BE REVEALED ONLY IN THE PRESENCE OF BARBICANE. LET US SEARCH FOR HIM.

THEY SOON CAME UPON BARBICANE...

WHAT IS THE MEANING OF THIS?

AN OFFER BY ARDAN TO REVEAL AN IMPORTANT PROPOSITION HAS CAUSED ME TO LAY MY GUN ASIDE. LET US LISTEN TO WHAT HE SAYS!

SINCE YOU BOTH DISAGREE ABOUT MY CHANCES TO REACH THE MOON, I INVITE YOU BOTH TO COME WITH ME ...TO THE MOON!

GO ALONG WITH YOU TO THE MOON?

WOULD THERE BE ROOM FOR THREE?

I WILL DESIGN SPACE.

PAST DIFFERENCES WERE QUICKLY FORGOTTEN IN THE INTEREST OF SCIENCE.

LET US GO TOGETHER, THEN! I HAVE JUST WORKED OUT A WATER FORMULA DESIGNED TO REDUCE THE SHOCK AT THE DEPARTURE OF THE PROJECTILE.

SEVERAL DAYS LATER, THEY PREPARED A PRELIMINARY WATER-SHOCK TEST...

IF THESE TWO ANIMALS SURVIVE THE SHOCK OF BEING PROPELLED INTO SPACE AND LANDING IN THE WATER, WE SHALL KNOW THAT WE THREE HAVE A GOOD CHANCE OF SURVIVING THE SHOCK OF THE TAKE OFF.

THE CAT AND SQUIRREL WERE PROPELLED ON THEIR WAY...

THE CAT WAS ALIVE AND SEEMINGLY HEALTHY...THE SQUIRREL WAS MISSING.

OUT IN THE HARBOR, MASTON AND BLOMSBERRY RETRIEVED THE SHELL...

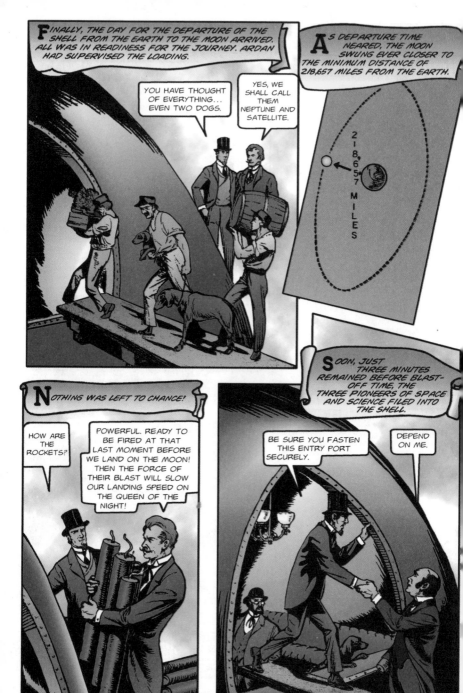

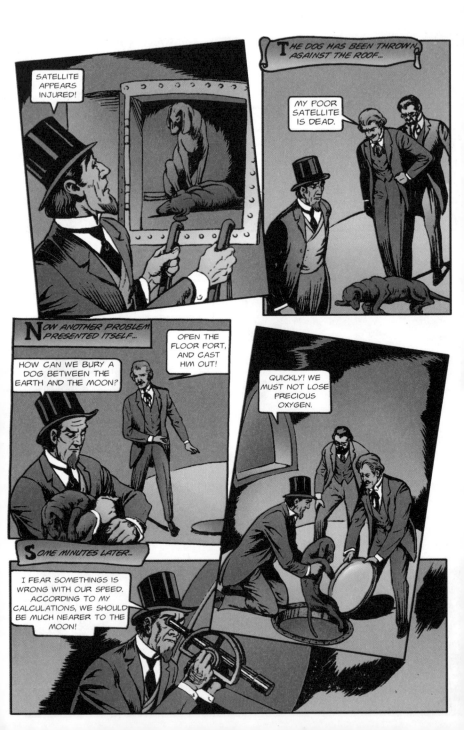

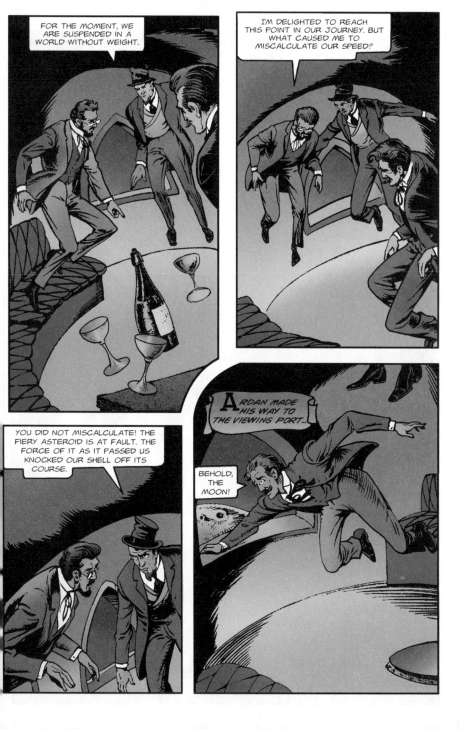

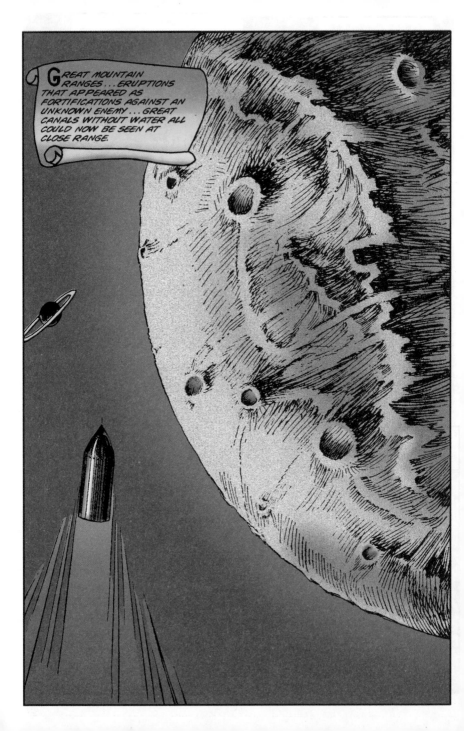

WE ARE NOW ENTERING THE MOON AREA WHICH IS BATHED IN SHADOWS.

THE NIGHT WHICH LASTS FIFTEEN EARTH DAYS!

THE TEMPERATURE IS DROPPING!

KEEP THE GAS LOW. OUR SUPPLY IS LIMITED. WHAT WE ARE ABLE TO SEE IS NOT ESSENTIAL TO OUR ARRIVAL.

OUR PRESENT SPEED SHOULD SUFFICE TO CARRY US INTO THE DAYLIGHT AREAS. MEANWHILE, THE HEAT OF THE GAS WILL HELP RELIEVE THE ACHING COLD WHICH IS BEGINNING TO SEIZE US!

DEATH BY FREEZING HAS BEEN MY GREATEST FEAR.

BE PATIENT. WE WILL SOON FIND LIGHT AND A SAFE LANDING.

MOVING INTO THE AREA OF DAYLIGHT IS NOT ENOUGH. WE MUST MOVE DOWNWARD! IF WE FAIL TO LOSE ALTITUDE, AND REMAIN SUSPENDED, WE WILL LIVE OUT OUR BRIEF TIME BEFORE DEATH CIRCLING THE MOON IN THE MANNER OF A MINOR SATELLITE!

IF BARBICANE'S THEORY BECAME FACT, THE SHELL WOULD CIRCLE THE MOON FOR ALL TIME. IT WOULD NEVER COME ANY CLOSER, NEVER TRAVEL ANY FARTHER.

WHEN WILL WE KNOW?

WHEN WILL WE KNOW? OUR FATE WILL REVEAL ITSELF WHEN WE HAVE RETURNED TO THE DAYLIGHT AREA. IF WE ARE NO CLOSER TO THE MOON THAN WE WERE BEFORE WE ENTERED THIS NIGHT AREA, THEN WE WILL BE SURE OF OUR DOOM!

BARBICANE'S SHELL HIT THE WATER WITH A TREMENDOUS SPLASH AND IMMEDIATELY SANK BENEATH THE WAVES.

RATHER, IN THE WATER, SIR.

YOUR MOON TRAVELLERS HAVE LANDED...ON THE EARTH!

A SEARCH PARTY WAS IMMEDIATELY LOWERED, BUT SEVERAL HOURS LATER...

NO SIGN OF THE MOON TRAVELLERS, SIR.

WE'LL STAND BY 'TIL DAYBREAK, AND WATCH FOR WRECKAGE!

LET US THROW OUT A BUOY MARKER, SIR. THEN, FAILING TO FIND ANY SIGN IN THE MORNING, WE CAN STEAM POST-HASTE TO SAN FRANCISCO, NOTIFY THE GOVERNMENT, AND PERHAPS RETURN WITH A SEARCH FLEET.

VERY GOOD IDEA, LIEUTENANT.

I WILL ALERT THE MEN TO PREPARE FOR A SPEEDY RETURN TO SAN FRANCISCO. MEANWHILE, IF OUR FRIENDS HAVE SURVIVED THE SHOCK OF FALLING FROM THE MOON, I'M SURE THEIR OXYGEN-MAKING EQUIPMENT WILL KEEP THEM SAFE FROM DROWNING.

LACKING WIRELESS TELEGRAPH EQUIPMENT, THE U.S.S. "SUSQUEHANNA" PUT ABOUT FOR SAN FRANCISCO. THE LONELY BUOY REMAINED BEHIND, MARKING THE SPOT WHERE THE SHELL HAD FALLEN INTO THE SEA...

UNDER THE SEA, THE SHELL SWIRLED AIMLESSLY WITHOUT A RUDDER. THE GREAT PROJECTILE WAS A PRISONER OF THE WATER, EVEN AS IT HAD BEEN A VICTIM OF THE FORCES OF SPACE!

AT THE NAVAL BASE AT SAN FRANCISCO...

WHAT'S THE MESSAGE?

IT SEEMS THE "SUSQUEHANNA" HAS MET UP WITH THREE MEN WHO WERE LAST SEEN ON THEIR WAY TO THE MOON!

THE STRANGE STORY WAS THEN TOLD TO THE ADMIRAL AT SAN FRANCISCO...

THANK YOU FOR YOUR REPORT, GENTLEMEN. I WILL NOTIFY THE DEPARTMENT OF WAR AT THE POLYGON AT ONCE. THE POLYGON WILL NOTIFY THE PRESIDENT. ACTION WILL BE TAKEN.

EXCUSE ME, SIR, BUT COULD YOU NOTIFY THE MEMBERSHIP OF THE GUN CLUB IN BALTIMORE?

AN EXCELLENT IDEA. I DARESAY, IF ANYBODY CAN FIGURE OUT HOW TO FISH THAT CONFOUNDED SHELL OUT OF THE PACIFIC OCEAN, IT WOULD HAVE TO BE A MEMBER OF THE GUN CLUB.

**F**OUR DAYS LATER. J.T. MASTON WAS ABOARD THE "SUSQUEHANNA"...

YOU WILL NEED SPECIAL AND HEAVY TACKLE, IF YOU PLAN TO LIFT OUR FRIENDS TO THE SURFACE! THE GROSS WEIGHT OF THEIR SHELL IS 19,250 LBS!

**E**QUIPMENT WAS QUICKLY ACQUIRED AND RUSHED ABOARD...

I HOPE MY FRIENDS ARE STILL ALIVE! WHAT STORIES THEY WILL HAVE TO TELL!

**T**HE RESCUE FLEET SOON PUT OUT TO SEA.

I TRUST YOU'LL ACCOMPANY US WHEN WE GO BELOW THE WAVES TO SEARCH FOR MY MISSING FRIENDS?

YOUR DIVING BELL IS MOST ADMIRABLE, BUT I PLAN TO CONFINE MY SEA DUTY TO THE SURFACE.

**F**OUR DAYS LATER, THEY WERE AT THE EXACT SPOT WHERE THE SHELL HAD GONE DOWN...

I WILL GO BELOW AND SEARCH FROM MY DIVING CHAMBER.

GOOD LUCK MR. MASTON! I HOPE YOU FIND YOUR FRIENDS.

FIVE HOURS LATER...

SHALL WE RETURN TO THE SURFACE, MR. MASTON?

WHAT ELSE CAN WE DO? THERE DOESN'T SEEM TO BE A SIGN OF BARBICANE AND THE OTHERS ANYWHERE!

NO LUCK, SIR!

HOW UNFORTUNIATE. NOW WE MUST CONDUCT A SURFACE SEARCH.

FIVE DAYS LATER...

NOT A SIGN! I'M AFRAID WE MUST PUT BACK TO FRISCO!

AHOY! I THINK I SEE OUR MISSING BUOY.

ONE MILE AWAY, AN AMERICAN FLAG WAS FLYING FROM A DIM OBJECT!

# FROM THE EARTH TO THE MOON
## JULES VERNE

The Author

Jules Verne was born in the port city of Nantes, France in 1828, the eldest son of a successful lawyer who specialized in maritime law. Verne's parents both loved literature and the arts, but they expected their eldest son to follow his father into the law. This didn't interest young Jules, who spent much of his time at the docks with his brother Paul, dreaming about going to sea and seeing exotic lands. At the age of eleven he stole away from home and signed as cabin boy on a ship bound for the West Indies. Unfortunately, his father overtook the ship before it had gotten very far, and the young Verne was retrieved. From then on, Jules was under strict orders to study for the law and put aside dreams of adventure.

When he was eighteen, Verne's parents sent him to Paris, where he passed his preliminary law examinations and

began legal studies. Though he was now beyond their immediate control, Verne still wasn't free to choose his own profession (unlike his brother Paul, who went to sea as soon as he had finished school). However, Verne spent much of his time associating with writers and theater people, and decided that the artistic life was the only one for him. When he completed his legal studies, he shocked his parents by refusing to return to Nantes and a position in his father's practice. He had been composing songs for plays, poems, and opera libretti, and one of his plays, *The Broken Straws*, had been produced by Alexander Dumas's Theatre Historique in 1850, when he was twenty-two. His parents were shocked, but there was little they could do about it. Although he could still not make a living at it, Jules Verne was launched as an author.

His plays were not very good—he wrote about twenty of them that have never been produced—but the next year he published a short story, "A Voyage in a Balloon," which shows his great interest in scientific matters (balloons large enough to carry crews

long distances were just being developed) and, of course, in exotic travel.

Verne couldn't make a living with his writing, and worked as a stockbroker as he began raising a family. But he retained his interest in travel, and kept the company of explorers and scientists. He became friends with a balloonist name Nadar who was building an enormous balloon, *Le Geant* (The Giant), with which he planned to make himself rich and famous. Verne decided to write a novel about a balloon voyage, and the two men ended up assisting each other's fortunes. Nadar helped Verne sell his novel, *Five Weeks in a Balloon*, to a publisher; and when the novel became a tremendous best-seller in 1863, its celebrity helped create publicity for the launching of *Le Geant*.

*Five Weeks in a Balloon* was an instant hit. Verne's tale of an expedition into Africa by balloon was everything his audiences wanted: a dashing adventure

made possible by technological breakthroughs that seemed to be just around the corner. Verne would employ this successful formula for the rest of his long career, which produced more than sixty novels. By the time he died in 1905, Verne was one of the most famous and beloved authors in the world.

## VERNE'S "VOYAGES EXTRAORDINAIRES"

*Five Weeks in a Balloon* was the first of a series of novels that Verne called his "Voyages Imaginaires," or "Imaginary Voyages." The 19th-century was still an age of exploration and discovery: although no new continents remained to be discovered, scientists and military expeditions were searching the interior of Africa, attempting to scale the world's highest mountains, and seeking to reach the North and South Poles. Crude submarines had been used during the American Civil War, and railroads were beginning to criss-cross the face of Europe and North America. A writer who could propose amazing new inventions, and show them allowing intrepid explorers to plumb the bottom of the seas, or fly through the air, or loft themselves into space—such a writer could capture the imagination of the reading public. Verne was the first writer to concentrate on new inventions as a subject, and he became one of the most popular writers in the world.

Although Verne wrote some romance novels and historical novels, his "imaginary voyages" were his most popular work, in his own time and today. In addition to *Five Weeks in a Balloon*, they include *From the Earth to the Moon*, *Around the Moon*, *Journey to the Center of the Earth*, *Twenty Thousand Leagues Under the Sea*, *The Mysterious Island*, *Around the World in Eighty Days*, and many others.

*From the Earth to the Moon*, published in 1865, ended with its heroes successfully launched into space. Verne wrote a sequel, *Around the Moon*, five years later, in which his readers finally learned what became of the brave astronauts. The two books are usually published today as a single volume, and the Classics Illustrated adaptation dramatizes both.

ARDAN MADE HIS WAY TO THE VIEWING PORT...

BEHOLD, THE MOON!

## THE FIRST REAL SPACESHIP

**Background**

There have been many tales of voyages to the Moon in Western literature. In 1638 Francis Godwin published a book entitled *The Man in the Moone*, which tells of an explorer who trains a flock of geese to tow an aerial carriage to the Moon. Daniel Defoe, best known as the author of *Robinson Crusoe*, wrote a 1705 novel called *The Consolidator*, in which a ship travels to the Moon powered by magical spirits. A pseudonymous 1728 satire called *A Trip to the Moon* described a lunar voyage that is propelled by gunpowder—a better guess than any other early writer made. But most tales of voyages into space were still essentially fairy tales or satires. It was only in the 19th-century, when the Industrial Revolution was demonstrating that mechanical inventions could perform wonders, that some writers began to treat voyages into space with a degree of scientific accuracy.

Joseph Atterley's 1827 novel *A Voyage to the Moon* may be the first lunar adventure that could be called "science fiction" rather than "fantasy," as Atterley's tale is told in a spirit of scientific speculation. Atterley's space ship, however, is powered simply by an anti-gravity metal; while Edgar

Allan Poe's 1835 story "The Unparalleled Adventure of One Hans Pfaall" uses a balloon filled with an imaginary gas lighter than hydrogen. Poe's carefully described voyage of a trip in a balloon seems to be the first story that actually made an attempt to describe how such a journey might be possible. Hans Pfall carefully calculates how long it will take him to reach the Moon at a speed of sixty miles an hour, and takes into account the fact that the higher one ascends from the earth, the thinner the atmosphere becomes. Poe got a number of things wrong, but his attempt at scientific authenticity was unsurpassed until Verne tried his hand thirty years later.

Although none of these writers suggest rocket power as a means to launch a space vehicle, Verne certainly came closest with his gigantic cannon. Verne cor-

# Five Things Verne Got Right

1. The weightlessness that travelers would experience when they're beyond the gravitational reach of earth.

2. Phases of the Earth—that the Earth, seen from space, could be "full" or "crescent" just as the Moon appears from Earth.

3. The fact that a flight to the Moon would be a major industrial enterprise, rather than an expedition that could be funded by a wealthy individual. Verne also guessed that this effort would come from the United States, rather than any of the advanced nations of Europe.

4. The use of rocketry to direct a space craft. (Verne did not believe that rockets had sufficient power to launch a ship into orbit—as indeed gunpowder rockets did not—but he was the first to propose rocketry as a means of travel in space.)

5. The appearance of the space vehicle as a sealed canister, from which the passengers could only look out through a strong window. Verne's "vehicle-projectile" is recognizably a space capsule, rather than a space-faring boat or carriage.

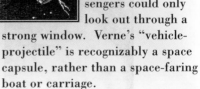

Engraving from the first illustrated edition (1872)

rectly deduced that a space vehicle would have to attain "escape velocity"—a speed fast enough to escape the Earth's gravitational field—and calculated this speed to be 12,000 yards per second, or more than 24,000 miles per hour.

This is, in fact, close to the speed attained by the Apollo missions that flew to the

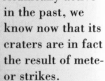
ACCORDING TO MY CALCULATIONS, WE CAN BOMBARD THE MOON WITH A GUN 900 FEET IN LENGTH, CAPABLE OF HOLDING 400,000 POUNDS OF HIGH EXPLOSIVES, AND DESIGNED TO FIRE AN ALUMINUM CANNON BALL WEIGHING 19,250 POUNDS.

"...THE DISTANCE BETWEEN THE EARTH AND MOON WILL VARY, BUT IT IS NEVER LESS THAN 218,657 MILES."

MOON

EARTH

# Five Things Verne Got Wrong

1. The feasibility of firing a manned projectile into space. Even with the cushioning mechanism Verne describes, any vehicle that was accelerated instantly from zero to 12,000 yards per second (more than 24,000 miles per hour) would mash its passengers flat. Indeed, such force would vaporize the projectile. (Verne probably realized this, but could see no way of getting around it.)

2. The "blazing asteroids," that seem to be flaming in the vacuum of space.

3. The "volcanoes" of the Moon. Although the Moon may well have been volcanically active in the past, we know now that its craters are in fact the result of meteor strikes.

4. The belief that the Moon was once inhabited, but that it "aged" faster than the Earth did, and is now a lifeless waste.

5. Gravitational interactions between small bodies (such as the projectile and the "second moon") are far weaker than Verne realized. Passing close to an asteroid-sized object would not deflect the projectile significantly from its course.

The interior of the projectile as illustrated in the 1872 edition of From the Earth to the Moon.

Verne was accurate on other details, as well. He realized that the best site in North America to launch a vehicle into space would be on the tip of Florida, and he correctly calculated how long a trip from the Earth to the Moon would take. He shows his scientists testing their design by first using experimental animals, and he was first to portray the weightlessness of space. Although Verne never gave a name to what he called the "vehicle-projectile," it can fairly be called the first spaceship in literature.

## A HIGH-SPIRITED FLIGHT TO THE MOON

*From the Earth to the Moon* is one of the most high-spirited novels Verne ever wrote. There is virtually no conflict or reversal of fortune in the novel: it describes, with nary a hitch or a problem, a visionary group's decision to build a cannon capable of firing a projectile to the Moon and their pleasure in doing just that. The characters in *The Mysterious Island* or *Twenty Thousand Leagues Under the Sea* may encounter dangers and setbacks, but the Baltimore Gun Club's heady progress in funding and building its cannon is uninterrupted. Even the antagonism of the decidedly unsinister Captain Nicholl (whose threat to the project consists essentially of public bets that it will fail) are unable to generate much suspense. Indeed, when the Captain challenges President Barbicane to a duel, the intrepid Frenchman Michel Ardan is able to reconcile the antagonists and persuade Nicholl to join the expedition!

In the sequel, *Around the Moon*, there are a few uncertain moments: an asteroid threatens to destroy the ship (although its glancing blow succeeds merely in killing one dog), and it ends up deflecting the ship from its course so that it orbits the Moon instead of striking it. But this, of course, allows the three valiant scientists to return to Earth, which they would otherwise not have been able to do. Another

AYE! AND NOT A SIGN OF WAR! PEACE, PEACE EVERYWHERE AND NOT ONE FIELD OF BATTLE WHERE A GOOD ARTILLERY-MAN CAN TEST HIS THEORIES ON GUNPOWDER, SIZE OF CANNONBALL, LENGTH OF BARREL, AND ALL THE OTHER IMPORTANT IDEAS SO DEAR TO AN ARTILLERY-MAN'S HEART.

novelist might have killed off one or two members of the crew in the course of their adventures, but Verne returns them safely to Earth, where the ship that picks them up finds them playing a quiet game of dominoes.

## JULES VERNE'S ADMIRING SATIRE OF AMERICA

Although Michel Ardan, who bravely volunteers to ride inside the projectile, is a Frenchman, everyone else in Verne's novel is an American. This was a departure for Verne, whose previous works had all had Europeans as characters. As interested as Verne was in the technical problems involved in firing a projectile to the Moon, he seems equally interested in the nation that he thought capable of achieving such a feat: the United States of America.

No reader can miss the satire in Verne's portrayal of the members of the Baltimore Gun Club. A pack of zealous militarists who care only for building ever larger and more powerful artillery (and plainly feel no concern whatever for the casualties of such weapons), they're in mourning for war, which gave them a reason for living. Pitcairn, the club statistician, estimates that on the average, each member had killed "2,375 men and a fraction." The joke about fractional men becomes yet more pointed when one considers the members themselves, most of whom are missing a leg or an arm or both, the victim of artillery experiments gone awry. Describing them in his opening chapter, Verne writes:

*Among their members they counted officers of every rank, from lieutenant to general, soldiers of every age, some making their debut in the profession of arms, others growing old over their gun-carriages. Many whose names figured in the Honor Roll of the Gun Club were now sleeping on the field of battle, and of those who had come back alive, most bore the marks of their unassailable valor. Crutches, wooden legs, hinged arms, hooks for hands, rubber jaws, silver craniums, platinum noses—no proof of combat experience was missing from their collection. Pitcairn had further calculated that the Gun Club could muster slightly less than one arm for every four persons, and only two legs for every six.*

The satire is grim enough, especially when Verne continues to underscore it in his opening chapter. ("'This is so demoralizing,' said brave Tom Hunter one evening. His wooden legs, resting on the fender of the fireplace in the smoking room, were slowly charring. . . 'And no war in sight!' sighed the famous J.T. Maston, scratching his gutta-percha skull with his iron hook.") The reader could be forgiven for concluding that Verne considered 19th-century Americans a pack of bloodthirsty warmongers, were it not for the admiring tones he expresses elsewhere in the same chapter.

"Now when an American has an idea," says Verne on his novel's first page, "he looks for a second American to share it. When they become three, they elect a president and two secretaries. Four, they appoint an archivist, and now they're in business. Five, they call a general meeting, and the club is officially constituted." There is no mistaking Verne's admiration for the initiative of Americans, which contrasts strongly with the Royal Societies and learned organizations of Europe, whose memberships were largely closed to ordinary people.

After President Barbicane gives his speech urging that the members of the Gun Club support his plan to fire a shell at the Moon, a surge of popular support sweeps the nation. "Seven days after the famous meeting of the Gun Club, the director of an English theatrical company, on tour in the states, announced that *Much Ado About Nothing* would open at a theater in Baltimore. But the people of the town saw in this title a snide allusion to Barbicane's project. They invaded the theater, ripped up the seats, and demanded that the unlucky director change his playbill. A man of wit, he yielded to popular demand. He replaced the ill-chosen comedy with *As You Like It*. For weeks afterward, he packed them in: Standing Room Only." Verne doesn't often show his comic sense in his novels, but he uses it to good effect here. He admires Americans' passion and spontaneity, even as he (like most Europeans of his day) considers their lack of decorum to be slightly barbaric.

## BUILDING THE GREAT GUN

Nearly all of *From the Earth to the Moon* is concerned with the effort of building the "Columbiad," the giant cannon

THE WHEEL SERVED AS A PLATFORM FOR THE MEN DIGGING OUT THE EARTH AND ALSO AS A BASE FOR THE STONES AND BRICKS THAT WENT INTO THE MAKING OF THE WALL OF THE GUN HOLE. IN THIS WAY, BOTH THE DIGGERS AND THE MASONS WERE ABLE TO WORK AT THE SAME TIME.

"techno-thrillers." But none of it is cutting-edge technology today, and these chapters now seem rather quaint. Most adaptations (in addition to the CI edition, Verne's story has been filmed on several occasions) cover the material swiftly.

that will fire the projectile. Verne devotes entire chapters to discussion of metallurgy, types of gunpowder, and the Moon's orbit. This was fascinating material to Verne's original audience; in a sense, *From the Earth to the Moon* is a forerunner of today's

Verne as satirist does make one reappearance: when he comes to the chapter in which the members of the Gun Club must decide whether to build their cannon in Texas or in Florida, Verne has the representatives of these two

THE REPRESENTATIVES OF FLORIDA AND TEXAS WERE HEARD. SEVERAL DAYS LATER, AFTER MUCH DELIBERATION, BARBICANE ANNOUNCED...

THIS DECISION WOULD STRAIN THE WISDOM OF SOLOMON. BOTH OF YOU OFFER SITES OF ALMOST IDENTICAL QUALIFICATION. HOWEVER, TEXAS OFFERS THE CHOICE OF ELEVEN DIFFERENT TOWNS WHILE FLORIDA OFFERS ONLY ONE. KNOWING THE FIERCE PRIDE OF NATIVE TEXANS, I FEAR THAT THE CITIZENS OF THE ELEVEN TOWNS WOULD FIGHT AMONG THEMSELVES FOR THE HONOR OF HAVING THEIR SITE CHOSEN FOR THE EXPERIMENT. THEREFORE, IN THE INTEREST OF INTERNAL HARMONY, WE WILL CAST OUR GUN AT TAMPA, FLORIDA.

states engage in a fierce rivalry, which includes insults, threatened violence, and challenges to a duel. (The Classics Illustrated version reduces this to one panel.) (See previous page). This violent burlesque does enliven the chapter, though it only occupies a few pages. For the most part, Verne expects his readers to be carried along by the zeal and enthusiasm that animates his characters.

It's only when President Barbicane receives the electrifying telegram from the dashing Michel Ardan that the book begins to liven up. What has until now been an engineering exploit suddenly becomes the tale of an expedition, which makes it much more interesting. As Verne scholar Walter James

# Michael Arden and the "Science" of Physiognomy

Verne's breathless description of the flamboyant Michel Ardan includes this passage:

*He had a head powerful like a lion's, and he tossed his long fiery hair like a mane. A short face, broad at the temples, adorned with a moustache bristling like a cat's whiskers, little patches of yellow beard on the cheeks, and round eyes a bit wild and myopic, completed this definitely feline physiognomy. But his nose was boldly drawn, his mouth particularly humane, his forehead high, intelligent, furrowed like a field never fallow.*

The word "physiognomy" today often refers simply to the human face, but for centuries physiognomy was a supposed science, by which an individual's personality could be deduced by studying his face. The idea that the shape of a person's nose could indicate boldness, or that a high forehead meant intelligence, may sound as foolish today as astrology or reading palms, but it's been around since ancient times. Aristotle wrote the earliest known book on physiognomy in the fourth century BC., and interest in physiognomy (along with palmistry, astrology, podomancy—studying the foot!—and other arcana) was widespread during the Middle Ages and the Renaissance. A roguish clown in Shakespeare's *All's Well That Ends Well* pretends to knowledge of physiognomy (which he mispronounces as "fisnomy").

Verne remarks about Ardan that "Disciples of Lavater and Gratiolet would have no trouble detecting on skull and face the unmistakable signs of combative-

Miller has noted, what began as an aggressive, military act—the firing of a projectile from a gigantic weapon—becomes the sending of a peaceful emissary. The novel has suddenly taken on a human dimension.

Jules Verne was a novelist of many talents, but vivid and psychologically subtle characterization is not generally considered one of them. With a few exceptions, Verne's characters are mouthpieces for his ideas, and have little imaginative life of their own.

There are virtually no women

ness, that is to say, of courage in the face of danger and a tendency to overcome obstacles; signs too of benevolence and a sense of wonderment, the instinct that leads certain temperaments to attempt the superhuman; but the bumps of acquisitiveness, the need to possess and acquire, were totally lacking."

Although many pseudosciences faded away in the 17th-century, physiognomy remained popular into the 19th-century, in part because of the work of Johann Lavater, whose works of the 1770s included illustrations of faces drawn to emphasize the points he wished to make. Louis-Pierre Gratiolet, who wrote in Verne's day, continued in Lavater's tradition; but physiognomy was disappearing, as more scientific studies of the musculature of the face began to appear.

Another pseudoscience persisted into the 19th-century: phrenology, prediction of personality according to the shape of the skull. The belief that different tendencies—toward wit, secretiveness, benevolence, etc.—were concentrated on specific parts of the brain's surface, and that the skull was shaped to accommodate these faint bulges, was popularized at the beginning of the 19-century by a German named Franz Joseph Gall. The "bumps of acquisitiveness" that Ardan significantly lacks were the product of what one of Gall's French disciples called the "sentiment de la proprietee;" Gall claimed to have noticed that pickpockets had bumps on this particular part of their skulls.

Although it was extremely popular for a time—by 1832 there were twenty-nine phrenological societies in England!—phrenology never enjoyed the status of a science, and its vogue had largely passed by Verne's time. Verne's apparent enthusiasm for physiognomy and phrenology suggest that he was more up-to-date in engineering and the physical sciences than he was in medical matters.

# The "Earth's Second Moon"

The tiny satellite that shoves the projectile off course in *Around the Moon* has a strange history of its own. In 1846 Frederic Petit, director of the French observatory at Toulouse, announced the discovery of a second moon of the Earth. It was observed by Petit and two others on the evening of March 21; Petit was not able to estimate the object's size, but calculated that it circled the Earth every two hours and forty-five minutes in a highly elliptical orbit that reached 2,150 miles above the Earth's surface at its apogee (the highest point), but came within a mere 20 miles at its perigee!

Scientists at the time didn't know how to calculate the effects of air resistance, so did not know that any satellite that ventured that close to the Earth's surface would undergo "aerobraking" from friction with the atmosphere, causing it to lose speed and fall to the Earth, perhaps burning up in the process. This may be what happened to this "satellite," which was never seen again.

M. Petit never lost faith in his "moon," and in 1861 he published a report that claimed to infer its existence from some unexplained perturbations of the Moon. This time he came up with different figures: a circular orbit of 4,650 miles above the Earth, lasting three hours and twenty minutes. Although other scientists did not pay much attention to this, the young Jules Verne was excited by the idea, and put it into his novel.

As a consequence, Petit's "second moon" became known to millions of readers. Although it was never seen, it has attained its own immortality as part of one of the best-read novels of the 19th-century.

in Verne's novels. *From the Earth to the Moon* contains not a single one; when the menfolk repair to Barbicane's house to eat sandwiches and discuss the cannon's design, we don't even learn if Barbicane is married! Although Verne was a social progressive who detested tyranny, lauded democracy, and admired America's policy of providing universal education to all children, he evidently was not much of a feminist.

Most of Verne's men charac-ters tend to be drawn with broad strokes, each with one or two traits that fully define them. Impey Barbicane is resolute and level-headed; J.T. Maston is nationalistic and impulsive; and so on. Although Verne wrote in an era in which the novel was reaching new heights of psychological realism—books published in the 1850s include Nathaniel Hawthorne's *The Scarlet Letter*, Gustave Flaubert's *Madame Bovary*, and George Eliot's *Adam Bede*—he seemed to have little interest in exploring character or the nature of personality.

Michel Ardan is not a subtle character, either, but he's certainly a lively one. Walter James Miller notes that he's clearly based on Verne's friend Nadar ("Nadar" is an anagram of "Ardan"), the flamboyant balloonist. Ardan's mysterious motives make for better suspense than the question of whether to build the cannon in Texas or Florida ever did; and his headlong embrace of any reckless action revives the novel at a point where it seems in danger of becoming dull.

The closest thing to a villain in *From the Earth to the Moon* is Captain Nicholl, who resents President Barbicane because the end of the Civil War cut short their professional rivalry at a point when Barbicane was ahead. This sounds rather petty (although Verne makes it clear Barbicane was being just as petty); but in practice, Nicholl does little more than serve as a devil's advocate, asking questions that compel the Gun Club members to justify their beliefs. Verne is careful, in fact, to show that Nicholl is not really worse than Barbicane. The scene in which Barbicane challenges Nicholl to a duel demonstrates this: in the CI adaptation the Captain pulls a gun on Barbicane; but in the novel, he merely calls him an "ignoramus." It is Barbicane who proposes the style of duel (about which Verne declares, "Nothing is more terrible than this particular type of American duel, in which each of the two adversaries hunts the other through the brush. . . and tries to shoot him down like a wild beast"), while it's Nicholl who is seen in the act of humanely trying to free a small bird from a spider's web. Verne makes it plain that, in the end, the Gun Club's President and his adversary are more alike than not.

### HANGING IN SUSPENSE

Both Verne's readers and his characters are left suspended by the end of *From the Earth to the Moon*. The force of the blastoff has disrupted weather patterns, so the observatory built especially in order to watch the projectile reach the Moon cannot see the sky. (See next page). By the time the clouds disperse, the ship has made it as far as the Moon, but is passing to one side of it, for reasons unknown. All the astronomers can say is that the projectile has passed close enough to the Moon to be pulled into its orbital embrace, and is now circling the satellite. They cannot tell whether the projectile will eventually crash into the Moon or will continue to orbit it forever.

The book ends with J.T. Maston proclaiming his faith that the three brave explorers will emerge from this alarming situation safe and sound. It's a striking point at which to end a novel, particularly because Verne had never

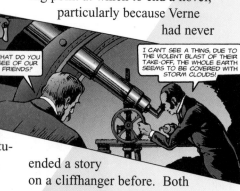

ended a story on a cliffhanger before. Both

# Verne and His Translators

Although Jules Verne's works have been widely available in English since the 1860s, the available translations are generally not very good. Because he was a best-selling author in Europe, Verne was translated quickly and sometimes carelessly. These translations—which tended to omit many of Verne's more complex features, such as his frequent references to Greek literature and his satire—made Verne seem like a simple, rather crude writer of energetic adventure novels. Ironically, this became something of a self-fulfilling prophesy: Verne is widely regarded in North America as a children's writer; as a consequence, new translations of his work are not often commissioned. The older translation remain in print,

and perpetuate the idea of Verne as a simplistic writer.

The best translation of *From the Earth to the Moon* is *The Annotated Jules Verne: From the Earth to the Moon* by Walter James Miller, published in 1978 and reprinted in 1995. In addition to the first complete and accurate rendition of Verne's text into English, it contains many footnotes explaining the historical and classical references in the novel.

There is no recent translation of *Around the Moon* available in English. Most editions use very old translations, which have sometimes been revised. The best available translation is the 1970 version by Jacqueline and Robert Baldick, which can be found in public libraries.

*Five Weeks in a Balloon* and *A Journey to the Center of the Earth* had brought their stories to natural conclusions. *From the Earth to the Moon* is only about half as long as *Journey*, however, and ends with the adventure just begun. It seemed obvious that Verne would write a sequel.

His readers had to wait five years, however, for the sequel to appear. In the years after *From the Earth to the Moon* appeared, Verne published *Journeys and Adventures of Captain Hatteras* (1866), *The Children Of Captain Grant* (1867-68), and *Twenty Thousand Leagues Under the Sea* (1870) before writing *Around the Moon*, which also appeared in 1870. By this time Verne was a more experienced and assured writer, and *Around the Moon* is a more dramatic and tightly-constructed novel than its predecessor.

Verne almost certainly intended all along to write a sequel to *From the Earth to the Moon*; what is surprising is that he decided to write two separate books in the first place. One reason has to do with French publishing practices in his day. Verne was under contract to provide his publisher with two volumes a year. This does not mean that he had to write two complete novels every year, however, for many of his novels filled two (or sometimes even three) volumes.

(*Journeys and Adventures of Captain Hatteras*, for example, was published in two volumes, and *The Children Of Captain Grant* was published in three.)

So French readers who bought *From the Earth to the Moon* in 1865 found nothing surprising about its cliffhanger ending; they could reasonably expect the sequel to follow in about six months. The only surprise was that they had to wait five years to get it.

## AROUND THE MOON: A CIRCUMLUNAR SEQUEL

*Autour de la Lune* (usually translated as "Around the Moon") is in many ways a better novel than *From the Earth to the Moon*. Set almost entirely inside the projectile—although Verne's characters gave a name to their great cannon, they never thought to name their ship!—the novel emphasizes both action and character: the projectile passes through repeated dangers, which Verne's three travelers must deal with. Where most of the dialogue in *From the Earth to the Moon* consisted either of one person delivering a speech or two people discussing some point, Verne now had to dramatize the interactions of three men in a confined space. As a result, the characters become less like mouthpieces and more like dramatic figures.

And this time Verne does

give his characters a major problem, which develops into a crisis. Although the projectile races toward the Moon on course, it soon encounters a second and much smaller moon: a satellite, evidently once an asteroid that has been captured by Earth's gravity, that orbits 4,650 miles above the Earth. The asteroid narrowly misses striking the projectile, and its gravitational attraction deflects the ship's course: it passes to one side of the Moon instead.

Verne's decision to have his aeronauts orbit the Moon, unable to land, then realize that they could use their fireworks (originally intended to slow their descent to the lunar surface) to nudge them back toward Earth is an inspired touch. Verne plainly felt uneasy describing what lay on the surface of the Moon, and landing his protagonists there would have required him to describe a landscape about which he knew he had too little knowledge. In addition, his voyagers had no way to return from the lunar surface, which would have ended the novel in exile rather than triumphant return. And in a story in which every other development went essentially without a hitch, this near-disaster gives the story some welcome drama. The aero-

nauts' voyage, in fact, very much resembles the 1970 flight of Apollo 13, which struck a meteorite on its way to the Moon and limped back to Earth after orbiting the Moon once.

More than a hundred and thirty years after it was first written, *From the Earth to the Moon* retains its ability to entertain readers. Why? The science is now out of date, its characterizations fairly crude, and most of the translations available in English aren't very good. Most other mid-19th-century SF novels are forgotten, including many (such as George T. Chesney's *The Battle of Dorking*, Edward S. Ellis's *The Steam Man of the Prairies*, and

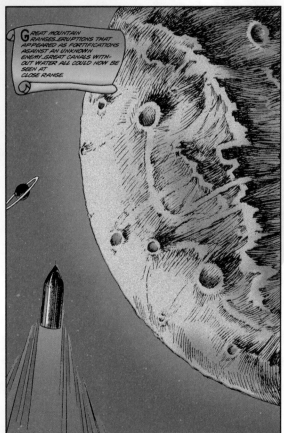

GREAT MOUNTAIN RANGES...ERUPTIONS THAT APPEARED AS FORTIFICATIONS AGAINST AN UNKNOWN ENEMY...GREAT CANALS WITHOUT WATER ALL COULD NOW BE SEEN AT CLOSE RANGE.

quaint and futuristic details should make the story fall apart; in this case, however, it makes *From the Earth to the Moon* curiously mythic: the characters seem to inhabit an imaginative realm outside history, like Norse gods or such archetypal figures as Rip Van Winkle. Even when the translation omits Verne's contemporary historical references, the reader can still respond powerfully to the story, which seems at once exotic and familiar. The other feature that makes *From the Earth to the Moon* memorable is that, despite its various wrong guesses and incorrect details, it succeeds in creating, for the first time, a real sense of what a space program would *be like.* H.G. Wells's *The First Men in the Moon* (1901), although it is in many ways a better written novel, contains plot elements—a lone inventor, a miraculous (and unexplained) scientific marvel—that had existed in science fiction since *Frankenstein* in 1818. Verne had already shown how out of date these conventions were. His rigorous rationalism, his appreciation of the technological

Edward Everett Hale's *The Brick Moon*) that accurately predicted future events.

One major reason is the story's peculiar combination of 19th- and 20th-century elements. Verne made a number of correct guesses about the future of space travel, yet his story is quintessentially of the 1860s: his "aeronauts" wear stove-pipe hats, and are shot into space by a tremendous artillery cannon, the high point of 19th-century military technology. This mixture of and engineering elements of his story, and his insight that space exploration would be an expensive and collective enterprise—these ring true today, in a way that all earlier writers (and the later H.G. Wells) don't. For all the errors in detail, Verne understood what space travel was.

•Verne's protagonists are an interesting mix: in some ways President Barbicane and Michel Ardan are similar (they both support the project from the beginning) while Captain Nicholl is unlike either. What characteristics do Barbicane and Nicholl share but Ardan does not, and which do Nicholl and Ardan share that Barbicane does not?

•Verne describes the interior of the vehicle-projectile in great detail (and most early editions showed an illustration as well), but mentioned no provision whatever for the three travelers to use the bathroom. Can you think of any other instances where the decorousness of Verne's day causes him to skip over some detail that a modern reader would quickly wonder about?

•Consider Verne's vision of the American spirit (exemplified by the members of the Gun Club, J.T. Maston especially) versus that of the Europeans (as exemplified by Michel Ardan). What are some of the virtues and shortcomings of each?

•The launching of the vehicle-projectile is attended by crowds of hundreds of thousands, who jam the towns and roads leading into south Florida. What are some other ways in which Verne anticipated the popular response to a manned flight to the Moon?

## About the Essayist:

Gregory Feeley is an essayist and science fiction writer whose reviews and essays have appeared in *Atlantic Monthly*, *The Washington Post*, and New York *Newsday*. His novel *The Oxygen Barons* (Ace, 1990) is set on the Moon.